Megan Kearney's

BEAUTY
AND
THE BEAST

For Blackbird,
Who is, thankfully, no longer
singing in the dead of night

Beauty and The Beast: Act Three
Copyright © 2019 Megan Kearney
All rights reserved

Published by The Quietly
First Canadian Edition

An alternate version of this material was originally serialized between
July 2016 and February 2019 at www.BATB.thecomicseries.com

Library and Archives Canada Cataloguing in Publication

Kearney, Megan, 1986-, author, illustrator
Megan Kearney's Beauty and The Beast: Act Three

Based on the works of Gabrielle-Suzanne Barbot de Villeneuve
and Jeanne-Marie Leprince de Beaumont.
Includes bibliographical references.

ISBN 978-0-9937212-2-9 (pbk.)

1. Graphic novels. I. Title. II. Title: Beauty and The Beast.
Act Three.

PN6733.K42M42 2014   741.5'971   C2014-902234-4

·ACT THREE·

BEAUTY
and The BEAST

· ENTR'ACTE ·

• ACT THREE •
CHAPTER ONE

Artemesia, Yew, Marigold

SHFF

...AH.

I SEE.

SIGH

...SO THIS IS HOW WE'RE DOING THIS.

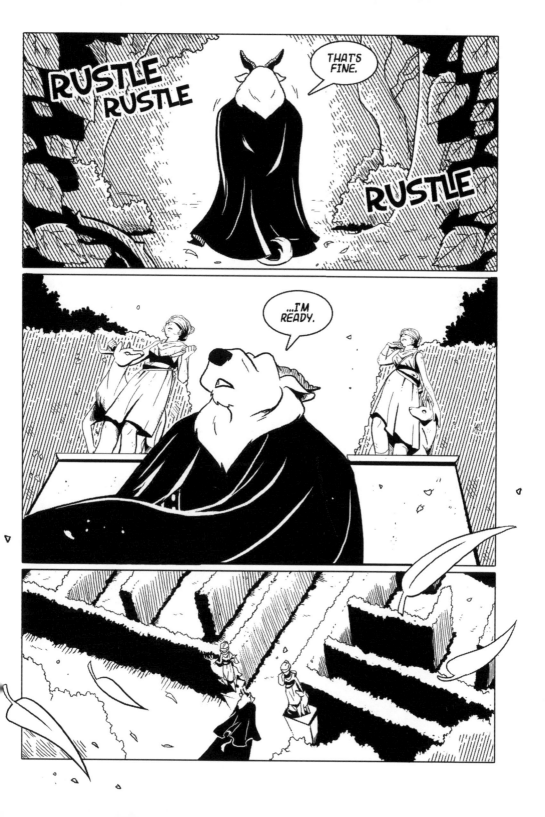

HEY.

OH!

...YOU'RE STILL AWAKE.

...JUST... THINKING.

...YOU'VE BEEN HOME THREE DAYS AND YOU HAVEN'T SAID MUCH ABOUT YOUR... TIME AWAY.

YOU **HEAR** ABOUT PEOPLE BEING SPIRITED AWAY, BUT I NEVER THOUGHT IT WOULD HAPPEN UNDER OUR NOSES!

I...UH...

YOU'RE... ALL RIGHT, RIGHT?

I MEAN, YOU'RE NOT RIPPED TO SHREDS, OBVIOUSLY, BUT...

YOU'D TELL US IF ANYTHING... Y'KNOW, **HAPPENED,** WOULDN'T YOU?

IT'S NOT **LIKE** THAT!

WE--

HE **WOULDN'T**--! HE **NEVER**--!

...

...HE'S NEVER DONE ANYTHING I DIDN'T WANT.

...

"HE"

...NOT THAT **BEAST** THAT YOU AND PA TALKED ABOUT...?

...CAN'T YOU LET ME PRETEND I HAVE A LITTLE CHOICE IN THIS?

PLEASE... PLEASE DON'T DO THIS.

DON'T *BEG* ME, ARGUS!

HAVE SOME *DIGNITY!*

LOOK AT YOU, THIS IS PATHETIC!

MAYBE HE IS YOUR FATHER, I DON'T KNOW. EVEN IF IT WERE TRUE, YOU'D STILL BE UNACKNOWLEDGED, IN LINE FOR NOTHING, AND LETTING YOUR MOTHER DRAG THIS CHARADE ON AND ON!

AND WHEN YOU'RE NOT TRYING TO APPEASE HER, YOU'RE LOST IN YOUR HEAD!

HONESTLY, A GROWN MAN WEEPING OVER THE DEATH OF A HOUND, WHAT AM I TO MAKE OF THA--

AT LEAST AORNIS WAS *FAITHFUL*

GRNCH

LET MY MIND WANDER AND IT ALWAYS FINDS ITS WAY BACK TO THESE DARK AND WELL-WORN PATHS...

GRNCH

GRNCH

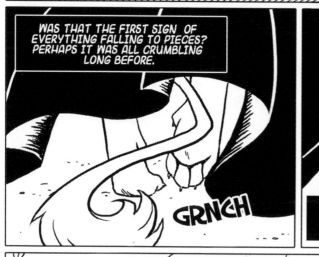

WAS THAT THE FIRST SIGN OF EVERYTHING FALLING TO PIECES? PERHAPS IT WAS ALL CRUMBLING LONG BEFORE.

GRNCH

I THOUGHT BY GIVING MYSELF UP I'D NEVER FEEL THAT SORT OF PAIN AGAIN.

THEY SEEMED INSURMOUNTABLE, THOSE SIMPLE, HUMAN TROUBLES...

BUT HERE I AM ONCE MORE...

PERHAPS, IN THE END, NOTHING IS SO CHANGED AS IT SEEMS.

NO.

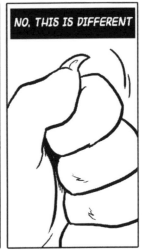

NO. THIS IS DIFFERENT

THIS IS A CHOICE I'VE MADE FOR A **REASON**.

TO MAKE THINGS **RIGHT**.

A THOUSAND SOULS HAVE SUFFERED HERE BY THEIR OWN CHOICES, BUT THIS WASN'T OF HER MAKING.

AND...NO MATTER WHAT COMES AFTER

I DON'T REGRET IT.

THEY SAY THAT A LABYRINTH IS A METAPHOR FOR THE SOUL.

THAT ONE FINDS ONESELF AT ITS CENTRE

BUT THESEUS FOUND THE MINOTAUR AT THE HEART OF HIS LABYRINTH...

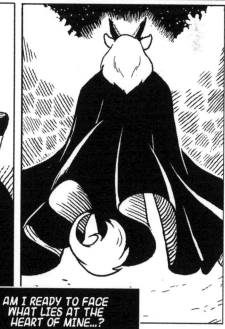

AM I READY TO FACE WHAT LIES AT THE HEART OF MINE...?

Chapter One: End

• ACT THREE •
CHAPTER TWO

Pansy, Motherwort, Helenium.

GRNCH

HAHH

...THOUGHTS GET MUDDLED...

HAHH

HAHH

GRNCH

...HARD TO TELL WHAT'S MINE AND WHAT'S BEING WHISPERED IN MY EAR...

STAGGER

WHUD

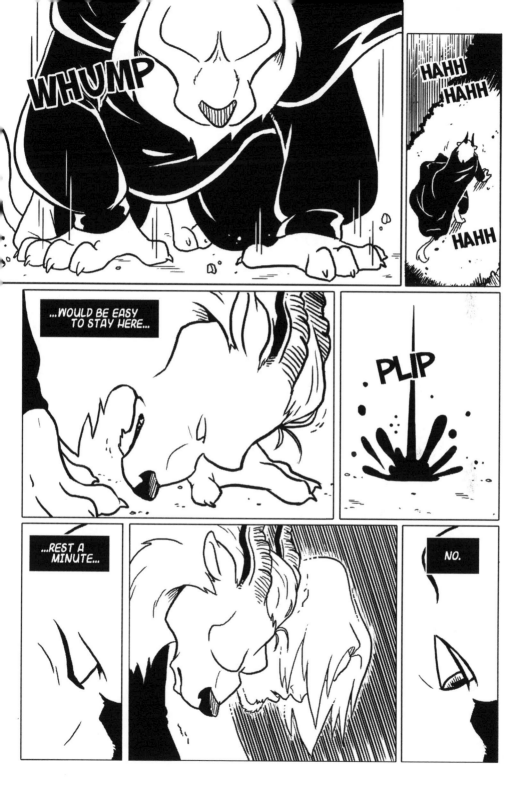

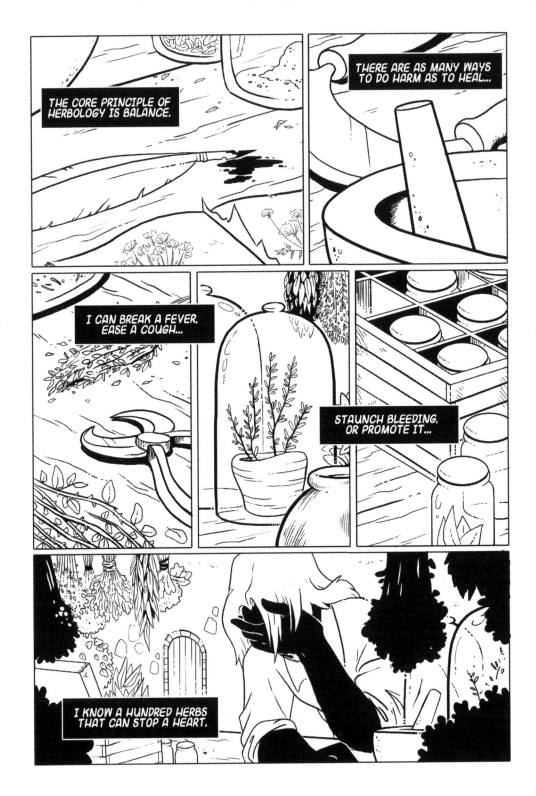

HEMLOCK, FOR EXAMPLE.

BOTH THE LEAVES AND ROOT ARE TOXIC

IF CONSUMED, THE RESULT IS PARALYSIS OF THE RESPIRATORY SYSTEM AND, IN MOST CASES, DEATH.

DRIED, IT LOSES ITS EFFICACY...

....BUT EVEN SO, IF CONCENTRATED IN HIGH ENOUGH DOSAGE...

BRBL

BRBL
BRBL

--HOW PATHETIC--

--KNEW THE BOY WAS WEAK HEARTED--

--BLOODY COWARD--

--A BASTARD CHILD IS ALWAYS AN INCONVENIENCE--

--THE SHAME OF IT--

--A MAN HAS TO LOOK OUT FOR HIMSELF--

--LOOK AT YOU, FOREVER BESET BY MELANCHOLY--

--IT'LL BE YOUR HEAD--

BE QUIET--!

JUST BE QUIET, JUST STOP--!

THIS POUNDING IN MY CHEST, IN MY HEAD--!

B-BMP

B-BMP

B-BMP

I JUST WANT IT ALL TO STOP--!

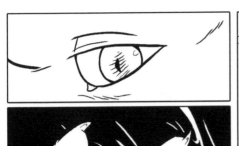

OF COURSE.

BACK WHERE IT BEGAN.

PLIP

...BACK WHERE IT ENDED.

ODYSSEUS FACED TRIAL UPON TRIAL TO RETURN TO HIS HOME... BUT WHEN HE GOT THERE, ONLY HIS DOG RECOGNIZED HIM. EVERYTHING WAS CHANGED.

SHFF

Chapter Two: End

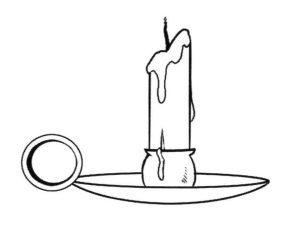

• ACT THREE •
CHAPTER THREE

Lobelia, Forsythia, Laurestine

LOOK, FALLING IN LOVE IS FRIGHTENING ENOUGH ON ITS OWN!

THEN YOU **DO** HAVE FEELINGS FOR SOMEONE, BUT THEY'RE NOT EXACTLY PRINCE CHARMING?

THAT'S **SCARY**, VEE! AND SHE'S GOT NO ONE TO **HELP** HER!

I...I WISH I COULD EXPLAIN IT ALL TO YOU, BUT I'M STILL NOT SURE MYSELF...

I JUST KNOW I'VE BEEN TRYING TO AVOID SEEING WHAT'S THERE.

...MAYBE FOR A LONG TIME, NOW.

I LEFT HIM THERE WITH NO ANSWERS. JUST LIKE I LEFT ALL OF YOU.

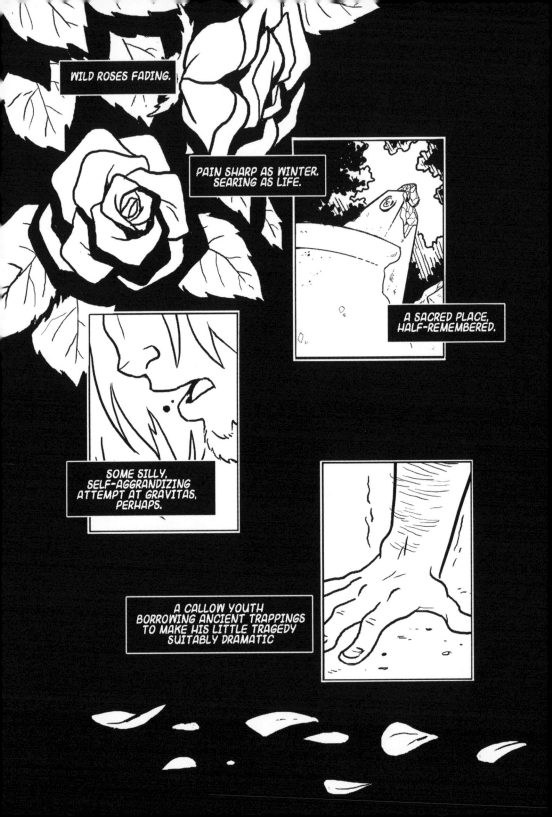

WILD ROSES FADING.

PAIN SHARP AS WINTER. SEARING AS LIFE.

A SACRED PLACE, HALF-REMEMBERED.

SOME SILLY, SELF-AGGRANDIZING ATTEMPT AT GRAVITAS, PERHAPS.

A CALLOW YOUTH BORROWING ANCIENT TRAPPINGS TO MAKE HIS LITTLE TRAGEDY SUITABLY DRAMATIC

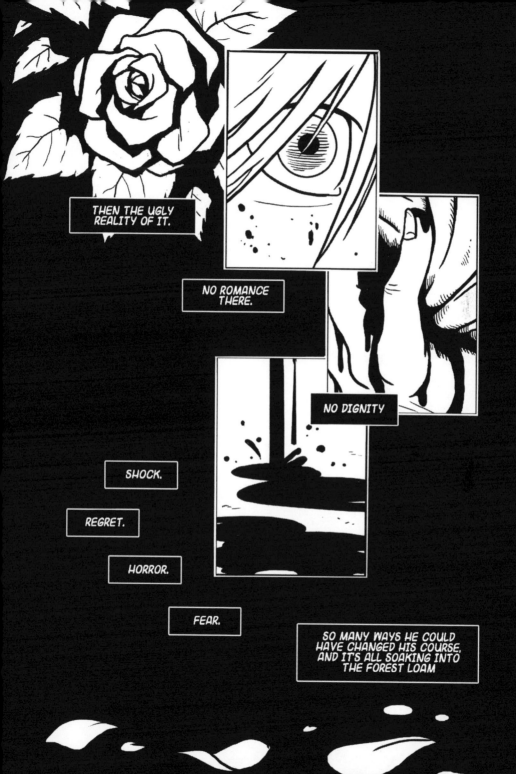

TUMP TUMP TUMP

HUFF HUFF HUFF

...ALL I HAD TO DO BEFORE WAS LOSE MY WAY...

HE DOESN'T KNOW WHAT
SNATCHES HIM BACK FROM
THE TEETH OF HELL

WHAT FERRYMAN HAULS HIM UP FROM THE ACHERON

BATHES HIM IN LETHE, LEAVES HIM ALTERED ON THE SHORE OF THE STYX

HE DOESN'T KNOW ANYTHING AND HE IS RELIEVED FOR IT;

LIKE EURYDICE SLIPPING GRATEFULLY FROM ORPHEUS' GRIP BACK INTO OBLIVION

A PERFECT SERVANT
SO LONG AS THE
NUMBNESS REMAINS

A FAITHFUL HOUND
SO LONG AS HE DOESN'T
CONTEMPLATE HIS ROLE

BUT WOUNDS
UNTREATED FESTER

FALLOW FIELDS
RETURN TO BLOOM

...EVEN A HEART
OF STONE BEGINS
TO CRUMBLE

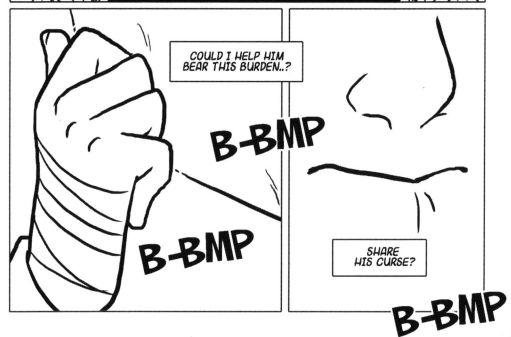

INSTINCT RUSHES IN LIKE A RAIN-SWOLLEN RIVER BURSTING ITS BANKS.

THE FRAGILE FACADE OF HUMANITY IN ITS PATH IS SWEPT AWAY AND DROWNED

HARD TO CALL SUCH A THING TRAGEDY WHEN ONE HAS LONGED SO FERVENTLY FOR THE DEPTHS

...AND TO FEEL
THE RAINS BEGIN.

Chapter Three: End

• ACT THREE •
CHAPTER FOUR

Hemp, Black Poplar,
Love-Lies-Bleeding

FLOWERS ARE SUCH LOVELY THINGS...

...SHOW THEM A LITTLE LOVE, THEY'LL OPEN FOR YOU.

...THAT'S RIGHT... THERE'S MORE HERE THAN JUST THORNS...

...WHAT IF THEY'RE NOT TRYING TO HURT ME...

WHAT IF...

PLEASE!

LET ME THROUGH!

...THEY'RE TRYING TO PROTECT **HIM**--!

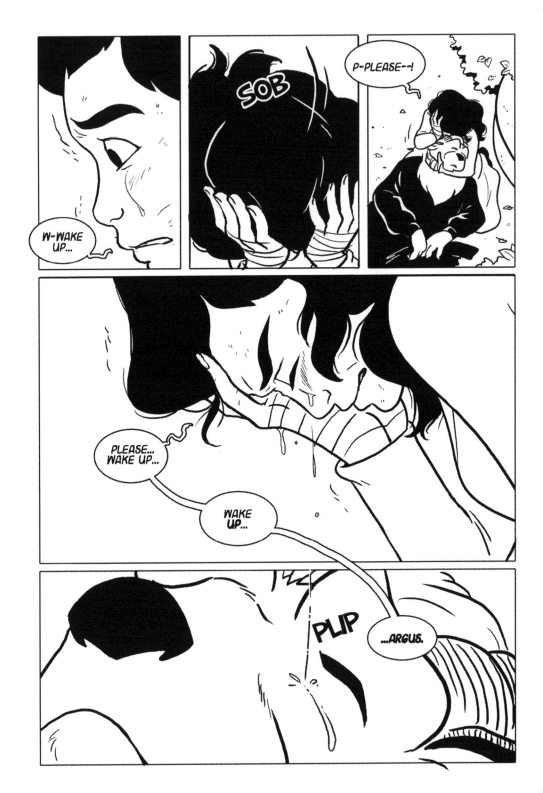

TK TK TK

Chapter Four: End

• ACT THREE •
CHAPTER FIVE

Roses

GROAN

GLUK

WHISPER
WHISPER WHISPER

I DON'T CARE ANYMORE--

WHISPER

I CAN'T DO IT--

TAKE IT, JUST TAKE IT FROM ME--!

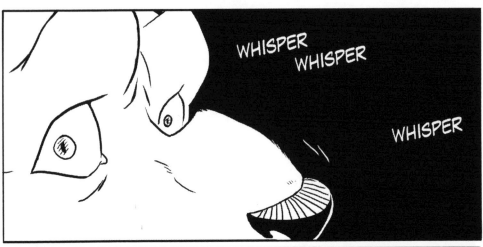

WE CAN ONLY LOVE THEM WELL AND STAND BY AS WE WAIT FOR THEM TO DECIDE WHETHER THEY SAVE THEMSELVES OR NOT.

OTHERWISE, YOU WILL BOTH BE DRAGGED DOWN.

FORGIVE ME IF I'M TOO PRAGMATIC. ONE FORGETS SO QUICKLY JUST HOW CAPABLE OF GRAND EMOTION HUMAN BEINGS ARE.

...THAT'S WHAT I FIRST LIKED ABOUT THEM.

THEIR LIVES FLICKER OUT SO QUICKLY, BUT THEY LIVE WITH SUCH PASSION.

YOU... YOU BEGAN ALL OF THIS, DIDN'T YOU?

WHEN YOU VANISHED THIS IS WHERE YOU WENT... YOU MADE A CONTRACT... AND THAT'S WHY PAPA FOUND THIS PLACE, WHY I CAME TO BE HERE...?

CLEVER GIRL. MY CONTRACT WOULD HAVE BEEN A SIMPLE EXCHANGE, BUT THE CASTLE DIDN'T ACCOUNT FOR THE FACT THAT IT HAD A VERY UNHAPPY AVATAR, AND THAT I WAS MORE THAN MERELY A MORTAL WOMAN.

IT TOOK WHAT HAD BEEN AGREED TO. THE REST REMAINS.

THEN YOU'RE NOT...?

YOU WERE NEVER...?

OH, DON'T BE ALARMED, DEAR ONE! IT'S NOT SO UNCOMMON.

I WAS FASCINATED WITH THAT BRIGHT EMBER OF HUMANITY.

MAGICAL THINGS... OUR HEARTS DON'T BURN SO HOT OR SO BRIGHT AS YOURS DO.

THEY LAST MUCH LONGER, BUT WERE COLDER... AND I WANTED TO FEEL THAT HEAT FOR MYSELF.

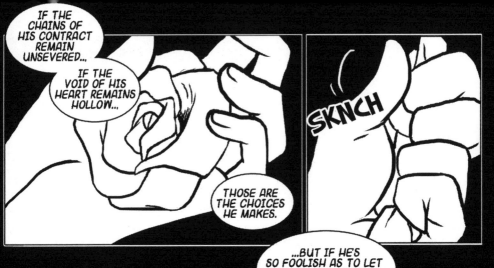

YOU'VE HAUNTED ME THESE LONG YEARS, IT'S TRUE.

I THOUGHT I WANTED TO ESCAPE YOU, BUT... MAYBE I NEED YOU.

MAYBE I NEED TO LEARN TO LIVE WITH YOU, RATHER THAN GIVE IN TO YOU.

MAYBE I'VE BEEN AFRAID I WOULDN'T BE A GOOD MAN.

FOR SO LONG I COULD SEE NO PATH THROUGH THE THICKET. I FELT FROZEN IN ONE WEAK MOMENT, TRAPPED BY IT....LIKE YOU.

AFTER ALL, I'VE BEEN A BEAST FAR LONGER THAN EVER I WAS ANYTHING ELSE.

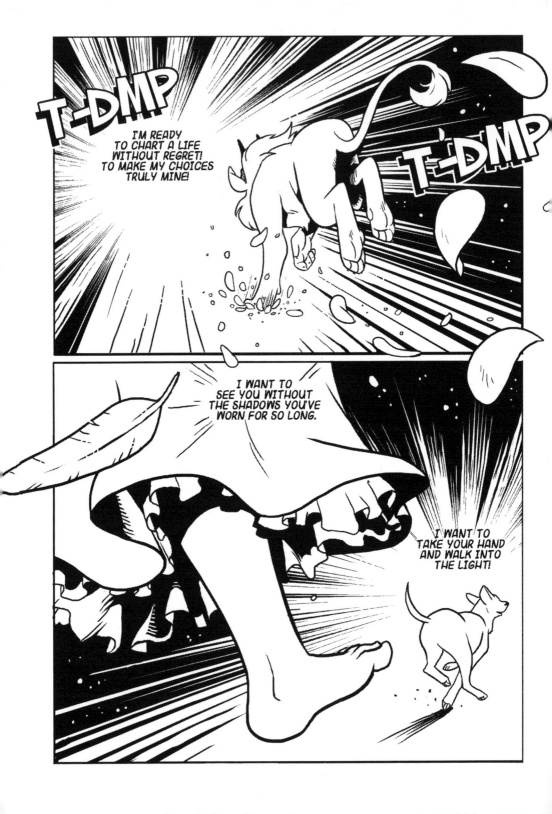

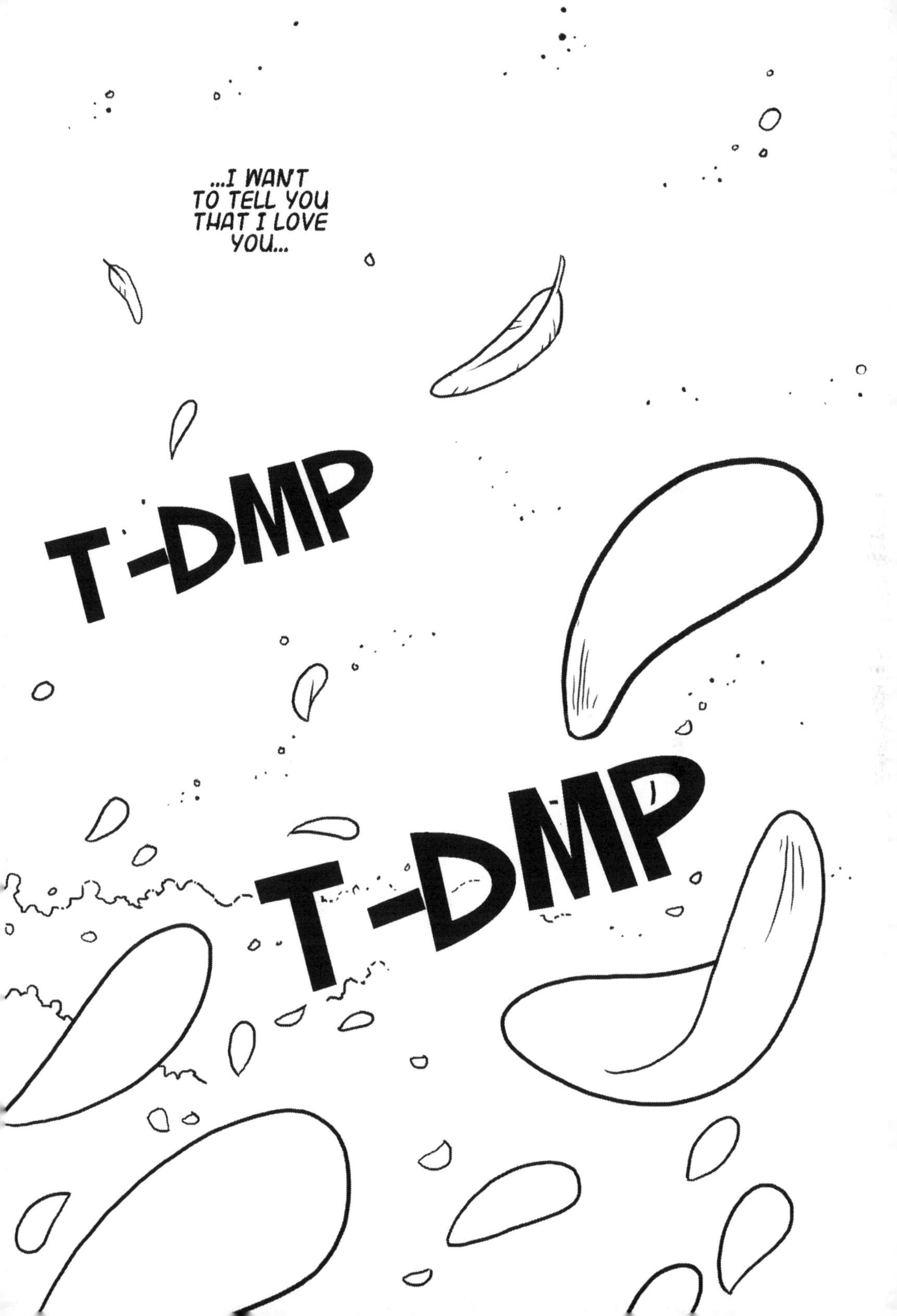
...I WANT TO TELL YOU THAT I LOVE YOU...
T-DMP
T-DMP

...WITH
ALL MY
HEART.

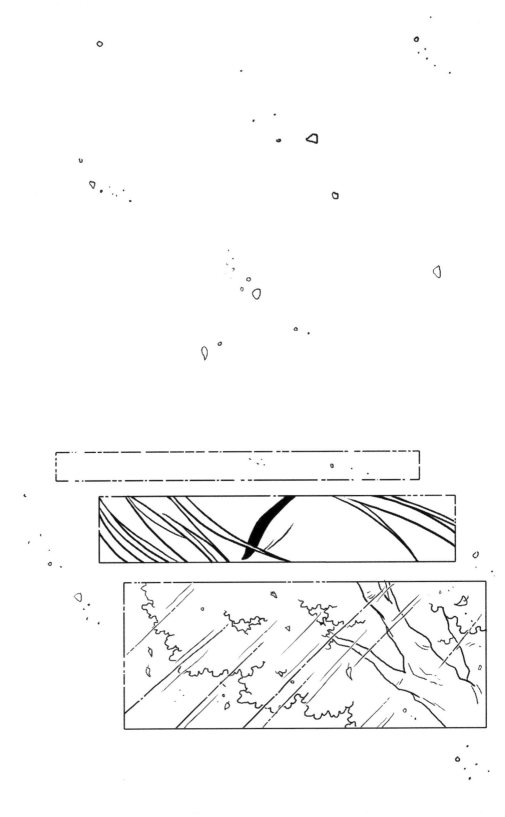

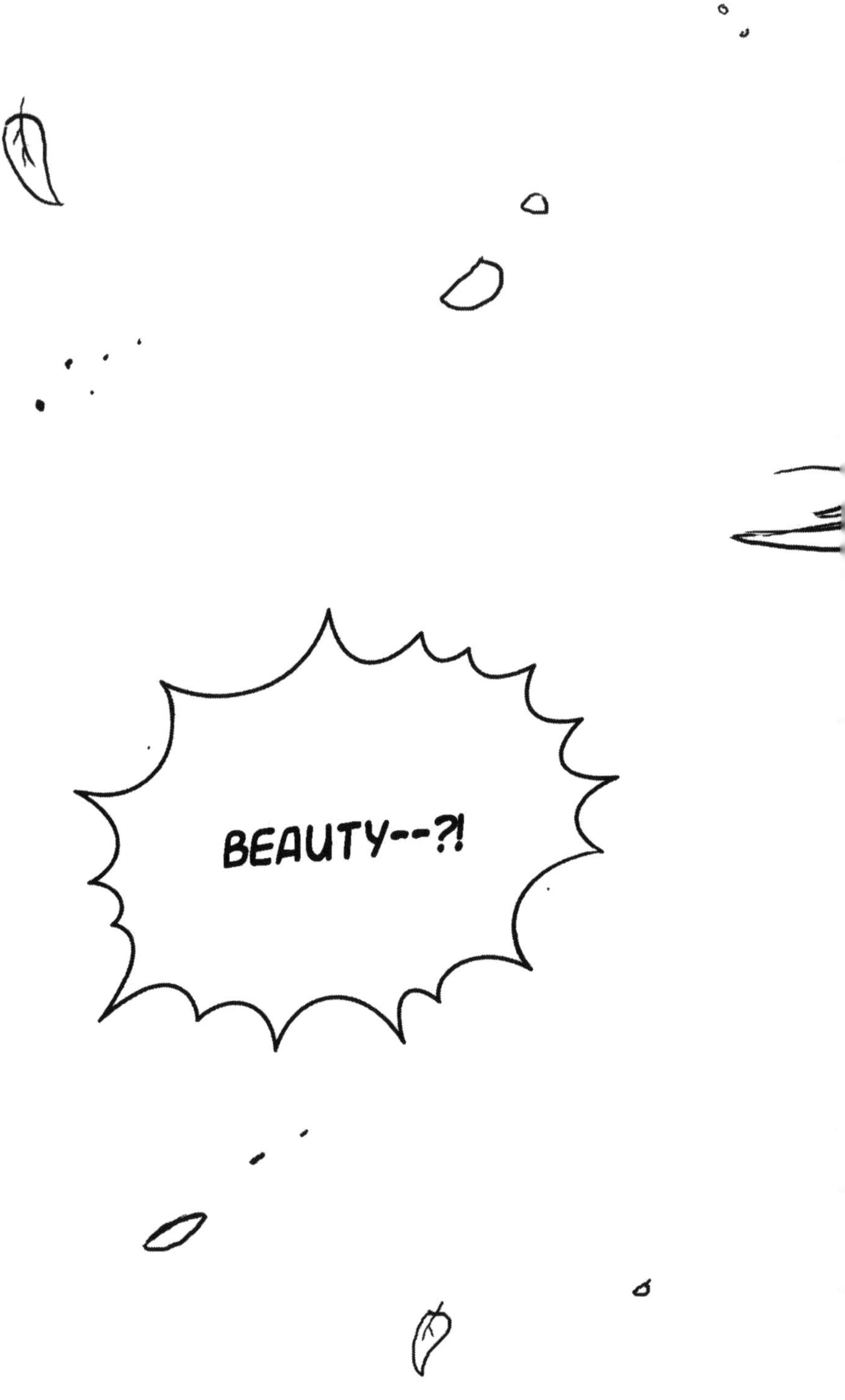
BEAUTY--?!

SHFF

• END •

• EPILOGUE •
A ROSE IN WINTER

TWO SWORN TOGETHER
IN A PROMISE

WE'VE CHANGED. THAT MUCH IS CERTAIN.

BUT IT'S THE NATURE OF LIVING THINGS TO CHANGE.

LIKE CLIMBING ROSES INTERTWINING, BETTER ABLE TO REACH FOR THE SUN.

THINKING OF VANISHING OFF INTO THE WOODS?
WELL... I'D BE LYING IF I SAID I **NEVER** CONSIDER IT...
HWOOO
...DO YOU MISS IT?
....
...SOME THINGS.
IT'S POSSIBLE I ALWAYS WILL.
...BUT TO BE HERE...
TIP

• Liner Notes •

The Language of Flowers

The language of Flowers, or floriography, has been a theme throughout my retelling of *Beauty and The Beast*. Imagine my delight when astute readers, following the story as it was originally serialized online, caught on to what I was doing. Watching the discussion of possible meanings and what they might imply for the coming chapter was a great pleasure for me, and, I hope, for the readers who took it as a mystery to be unravelled. Interpretations of flowers and their symbolism varies between cultures and locales, so for the curious, the following meanings may be inferred.

Artemesia - Absence
Bay leaves -victory, resurrection, wisdom
Black Poplar - courage, endurance
Forsythia - Anticipation
Helenium - unfortunate love/tears
Hemlock - death
Hemp - purity/fate
Lilac - First Feelings of Love
Laurestine -I die if neglected
Love-lies-Bleeding - Hopeless, not heartless
Lobelia - Malevolence
Marigold- Grief, mourning and despair
Motherwort - Concealed or secret love
Pansy - You Occupy my Thoughts
Roses- Love
Yew - Sorrow

The Language of Roses

Floriography has been a visual motif throughout my retelling of *Beauty and The Beast*, and it would not have been so without the iconic stolen rose of the original tale. We don't know why Villeneuve chose a rose for Beauty's wish, starting the chain of events that eventually bring our heroine to the Beast's palace. Variations on the tale often feature a tree branch, a sprig of rosemary, or even a bird as her request. But we do know that roses have carried many meanings over the years.

With their showy blooms and thorn-decked canes, roses make for a potent metaphor. They are associated with the Virgin Mary in Christian tradition, the white rose in particular symbolizing her purity, and with the goddess Aphrodite in Greco-Roman religion. The consumption of holy rose petals breaks the curse that has transformed the character Lucius in the writings of ancient Roman author Apuleius.

Aside from being one one of the most mythologized flowers, Roses have a wealth of meaning and symbolism assigned to them in many cultures. For example, yellow roses, often said to connote friendship in western circles, carry a double meaning of jealousy and infidelity in Muslim culture. In England, the red-and-white striped rose, indicating unity, is also a symbol of the peace between the long-warring Lancaster and York houses, whose heraldry respectively depicted the red and white rose.

The Language of Roses

In the Language of Flowers, the rose is always associated with love, but its colour and state of bloom offer nuance. A flower in full bloom carries a deeper meaning than a young or immature blossom. A bi-colour rose can suggest a mingling of meanings, such as the yellow rose streaked with red symbolizing the growth of friendship to love. Various breeds of rose are said to carry unique meanings as well, such as the dog rose indicating pleasure and pain, or the tea rose indicating gallantry. The number of roses can also be assigned meaning (and a hefty price tag).

For the sake of simplicity, these are the most commonly assigned meanings of various colours of rose.

Red - Romantic Love, admiration or respect
White -Purity, innocence, sympathy
Pale pink - Innocent love, admiration
Bold pink - Gratitude and appreciation
Yellow - Friendship and warmth
Orange - Passion, enthusiasm
Salmon - Desire, excitement
Cream - Charm, consideration
Lavender - Adoration or enchantment
Green - Prosperity
Black - Death or an ending

Acknowledgements

Beauty and The Beast has been a twice weekly commitment for more than seven years, a project I spent more of my twenties working on than not. It's been by my side as I went from a new graduate to an established professional. It has opened doors I never dreamed possible, and taught me a great deal-- not just about the art of storytelling, but about myself, and the person I want to become. I owe a many thanks to many people, but most notably...

Rachel Kahn, who sat me down and said "you're not laying this book out in photoshop again, I'm teaching you publishing software"

The team at Comic Book Embassy, who are always there to offer support, advice and resources. I love you guys.

To Blackbird, who was born sometime during Chapter Two of this book, and who was strapped to me while I drew much of it in a haze of exhaustion and lactation. Thank you for sleeping at night now.

As ever, to Nick, who shoulders so many burdens so I don't have to, and who has encouraged me from the very beginning. It's finally done. I promise I'll try to make the next one earn money.

And to all of you, Dear Readers, for coming with me on this journey!

Megan Kearney is a Canadian author and illustrator,
and the manager of Comic Book Embassy, a busy co-work
studio located in the heart of Toronto's Chinatown.
She has contributed to many collections and is a writer
on the *Disney Princess* series. *Beauty and The Beast* was her first
completed comic project. she lives with her husband and
son in Toronto, where they will never be able to afford a home.